Foreword

Debra Williams grew up in a lo two siblings, in close proximity to Aunts, Uncles and Cousins on her Father's and Mother's side.

Outside of her parents, her biggest influence was her maternal Grandmother, Ivy. "Mama'" as she was called, offered welcoming arms that protected anyone who needed safety, and a kitchen that nourished all who entered it.

Spending summers and holidays with Mama taught Debra about the importance of listening and how essential empathy is for lasting connections.

As the thought leader of the family, Mama always made her home a place for everyone to express themselves, and gave structure to conversations about growing up and living in a complicated world.

Debra's Mother, Yvonne, displayed the same traits, continuing to make the two safest words in the world, 'home' and 'family'. Both had impressive taste in clothes, and completed their personal style with eye-catching hats.

This story is a tribute to both of them.

CHURCH HAT

My Mama has a closet
where she keeps all her crowns
In boxes and on faceless heads
on shelves, not on the ground

"Crowns" are what she calls her hats
She wears on special days
The church ones are the fanciest
designed in different ways

They come in every color
and sizes, except small
With bows and gems and feathers
for an outfit that's formal

Some are made of rigid straw
with wide brims like a plate

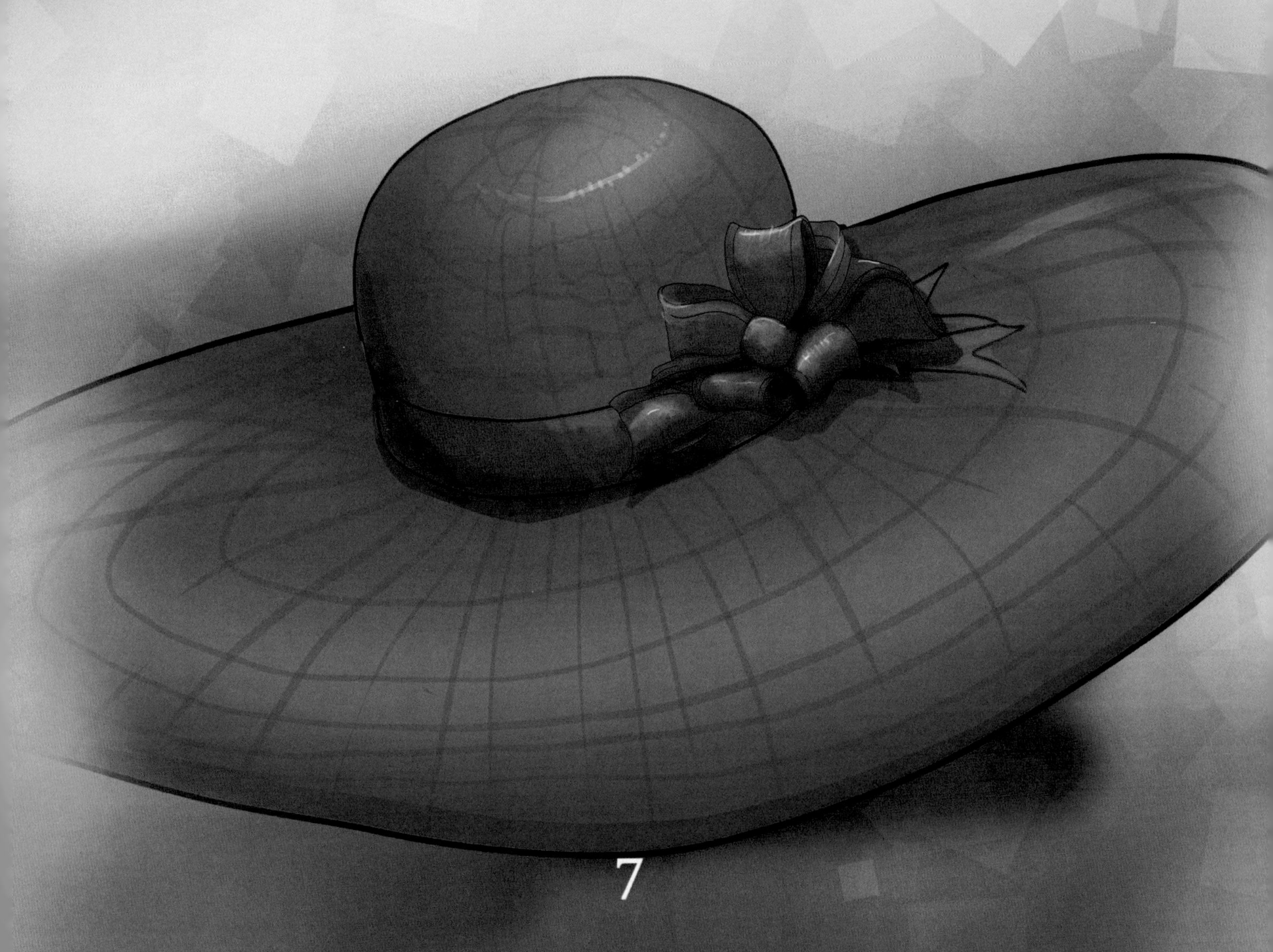

Three of them have unique shapes for her to fascinate

I like the way that Mama looks
in crowns that block the sun
The black one is for funerals
I never touch that one

One day when Mama was not home
or so I thought, I went
upstairs to try on the new hat
that she had bought for Lent

Distracted, I was posing with
hands set on my hips
She came into the room and said
"My goodness, what is this?"

I froze in guilt and panic
not knowing what to do
It meant the world when Mama said
"You know that I love you"

"But sweetheart, these hats are for me,
not playthings, like your toys
My crowns are for grown ladies
not meant for little boys."

She knelt before me slowly
Looked at me for awhile
And then said, with a steady gaze
'You have a unique style."

"I know," I said, frustrated
"I want to wear hats too
and go to church with my own crown
dressed up to look like you!"

She smiled and held her hat in hand
"How about a compromise?
We'll go together to the store
and buy one, customized"

"You pick the color and the shape
and a new outfit too
While we keep talking honestly
about what you're going through"

"You are my child, I am your Mom
we won't always agree
But I will listen and advise
You're always safe with me"

"You have time to grow and thrive
We don't want you to hide
you should always be yourself
We're always on your side"

" Soon you will be an adult and live your best life, yet until then we will discuss what is appropriate."

I understood what Mama said
and put her crown away
We hugged and went out to the store
and bought my hat that day!

The more I understand myself
I know my parents will,
Wrap arms of love around me
as I mature to build
A life that's true to who I am
taking steps every day,
to adult independence
when I can live my way

Now I have a shelf with crowns
made just for me so that
Both Mama and I show our style
Dressed up in our church hats.

Debra Williams is an empowerment coach and performance strategist whose consulting practice specializes in leadership mentoring. She was raised in a Caribbean household and moved with her family to Canada as a young adult where she developed an unexpected love of winter sports. Debra attended university in the United States of America and completed her Bachelor and Master's degrees while working in environmental conservation and regulatory compliance before returning to Toronto, Ontario. After years of career advancement, she decided to write her first book in tribute to the women who influenced her the most.

Follow her publication journey at:

www.mybestlifebooks.ca
www.mybestlifebooks.com

Instagram @mybestlifebooks
Twitter @mybestlifebooks

www.linkedin.com/company/debrawilliamsconsulting

ISBN: 978-1-7778908-0-3 (Paperback)

Author: Debra Williams

Front Cover Illustration by Janine Carrington

For Ivy and Yvonne

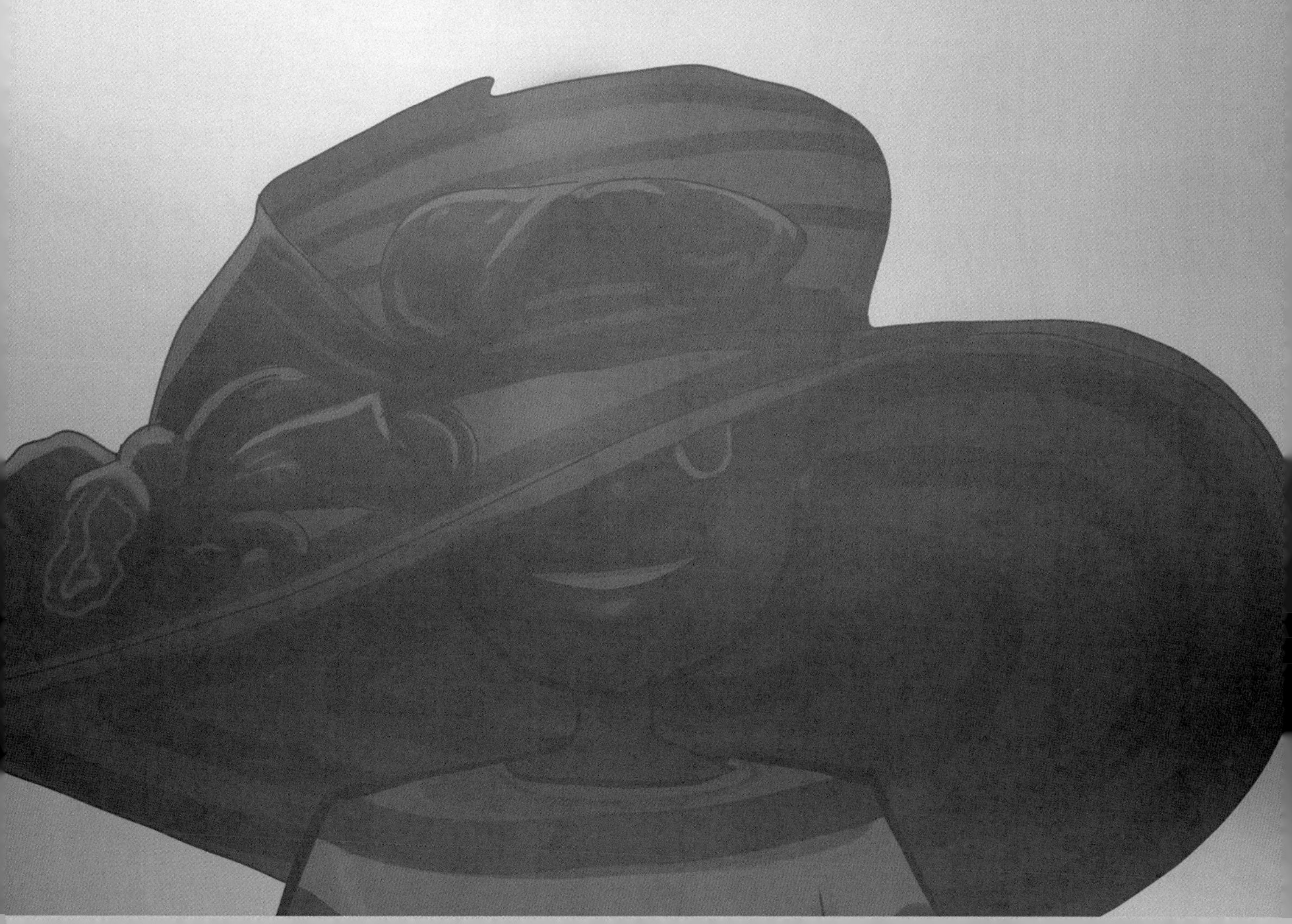